This Abominable Book Belongs To:

____

The Abominable Charles Christopher
Book One

www.abominable.cc

Published by Abominable Books
5333 Ave. Casgrain
Suite 606
Montreal, QC
H2T 1X3

ISBN: 978-0-9866131-1-1
First Softcover Edition: October 2011

PRINTED IN CANADA

THE ABOMINABLE CHARLES CHRISTOPHER

BY KARL KERSCHL

PLIP

KRA-KOOM

SPLISH SPLISH SPLISH

HEY.

AT LEAST IT'S NOT MORE *SNOW,* RIGHT?

I MEAN, IT'LL JUST BE FREEZING AGAIN TOMORROW, SO WE SHOULD ENJOY THIS WHILE IT LASTS. ***ESPECIALLY*** WITH THAT CUSHY SPOT ***YOU'VE*** GOT.

ANYWAY, BUDDY, I'VE GOTTA' ***FLY.***
NICE TALKIN' TO YA'!

OH! AND THERE'S A ***PARTY*** TONIGHT AT ***VIVOL'S.***
IN CASE YOU HADN'T HEARD...

PLIP
SHAKE
SHAKE
SHAKE
GRUMBLE

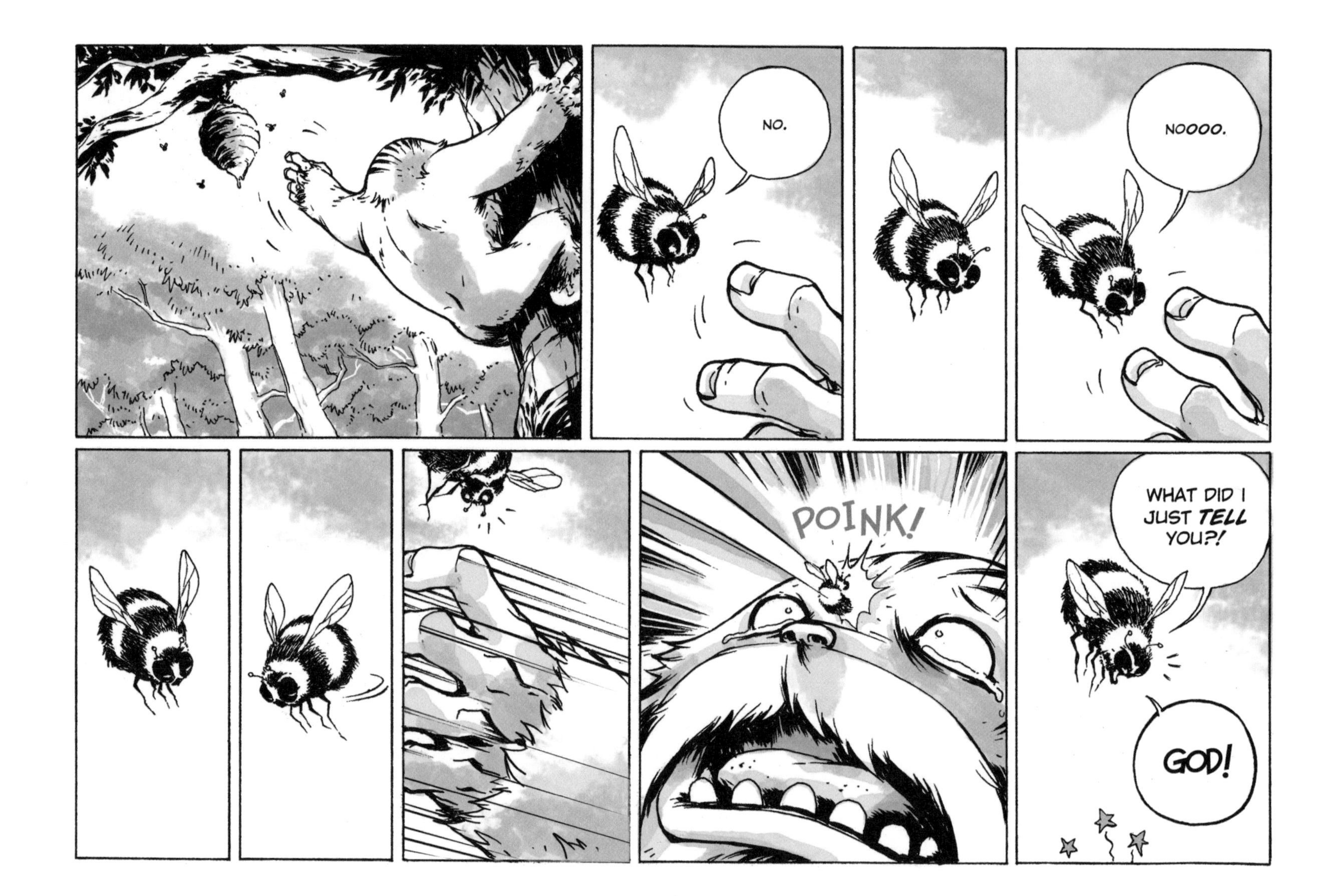
NO.
NOOOO.
POINK!
WHAT DID I JUST *TELL* YOU?!
GOD!

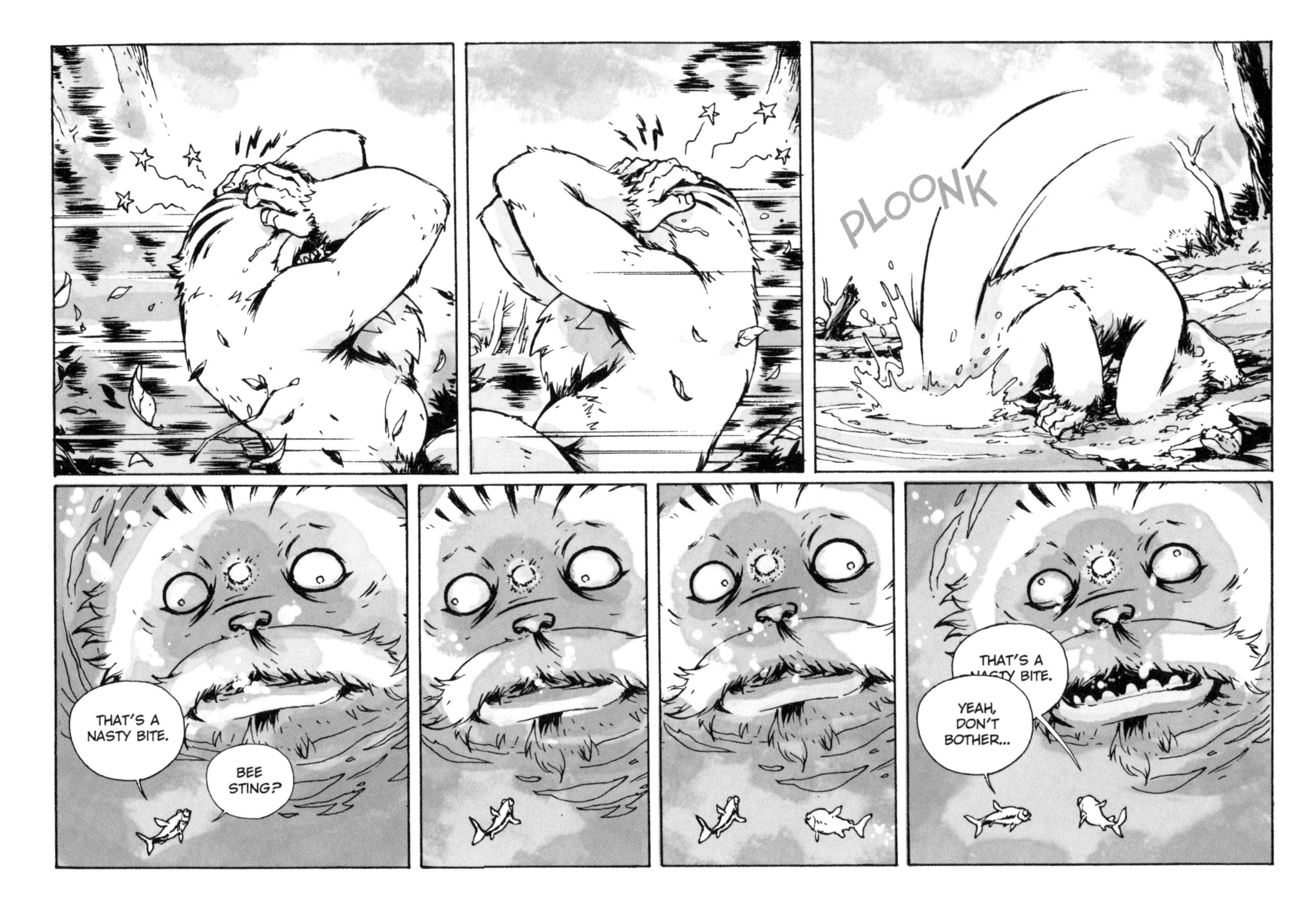
PLOONK
THAT'S A NASTY BITE.
BEE STING?
THAT'S A NASTY BITE.
YEAH, DON'T BOTHER...

OKAY, HONEY! WE'RE HEADING OVER TO VIVOL'S NOW!
OKAY! HAVE FUN! DON'T BE OUT TOO LATE!
I WON'T!
AND DON'T DRINK TOO MUCH!
I WON'T! JEEZ!
KISS.
PECK

VIVOL!
GREAT PARTY, MAN!

FRIENDS.
THANK YOU FOR COMING TO PARTY OF VIVOL.

EVERYONE HAS FULL STOMACH AND ALL IS GOOD...
...BUT TIME IS NOW FOR SERIOUS TALK.
CEDAR FOREST IS HOME TO ALL ANIMALS.
IS HOME TO VIVOL ALSO FOR MANY YEARS.

BUT NOW, IN TURNING OF SEASON, IS COME TERRIBLE--

PSSSST PSSS...

FOOD AND REFRESHMENT PROVIDED BY SISSI SKUNK, OF SOUTH-BEND-IN-THE-RIVER.

...BUT NOW, IN TURNING OF SEASON, IS COME TERRIBLE DANGER.
LISTEN WELL. I TELL YOU...

HOP
HOP

SON OF A...!!
SNAP!

HAM
AM
AM
AM
WHAM
WHAM

ZZZ...
ZZMFF...
I'LL HAVE S'MORE OF THOSE TURNIPS IF Y'RE OFFERING...
...SNRRK
RUSTLE RUSTLE
SNAP!
ZZZ
...DON'T MIND IF I DO...

COME IN
COME IN
COME IN
COME IN

THUMP
THUMP
THUMP

SIGH.

SON?
SON, I WANT YOU TO LOOK AT SOMETHING FOR A MINUTE.
WHAT DO YOU SEE?
AN IDIOT, SON. HE'S AN IDIOT.
GOT NO DIRECTION, RUNNING AROUND LIKE THAT. GOING IN CIRCLES.

...

...I DON'T KNOW, DAD. WHAT *IS* HE?
THUMP
BOP

...

DOESN'T ***UNCLE TIMO*** RUN AROUND IN CIRCLES SOME-TIMES?

YOUR UNCLE TIMO'S CRAZY, SON.
THERE'S A DIFFERENCE.

FLAP
FLAP
FLAP
FLAP
THUMP!
CLATTER

CRASH!

♪♪

WAAAAHHHHHH... I GOT THE SPINS!
DON'T TALK TO ME.

WHAT DO YOU THINK OF VIVOL'S WARNING?
I THINK HE WORRIES TOO MUCH.

PANT
GASP

FWOOOMP!

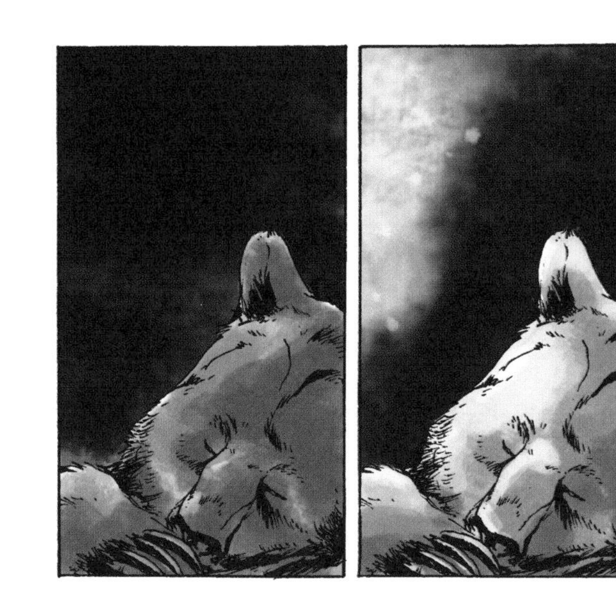

MOON BEAR?

the STORY of
VIVOL & MOON BEAR
part one

AI! MASHA! GET UP!
MAMA?

COME ON, LAZY PIG!
TIME FOR SHOW!
CLANK

DO NOT WORRY, VIVOL.
MAMA IS WITH YOU.

MAMA IS WITH YOU.

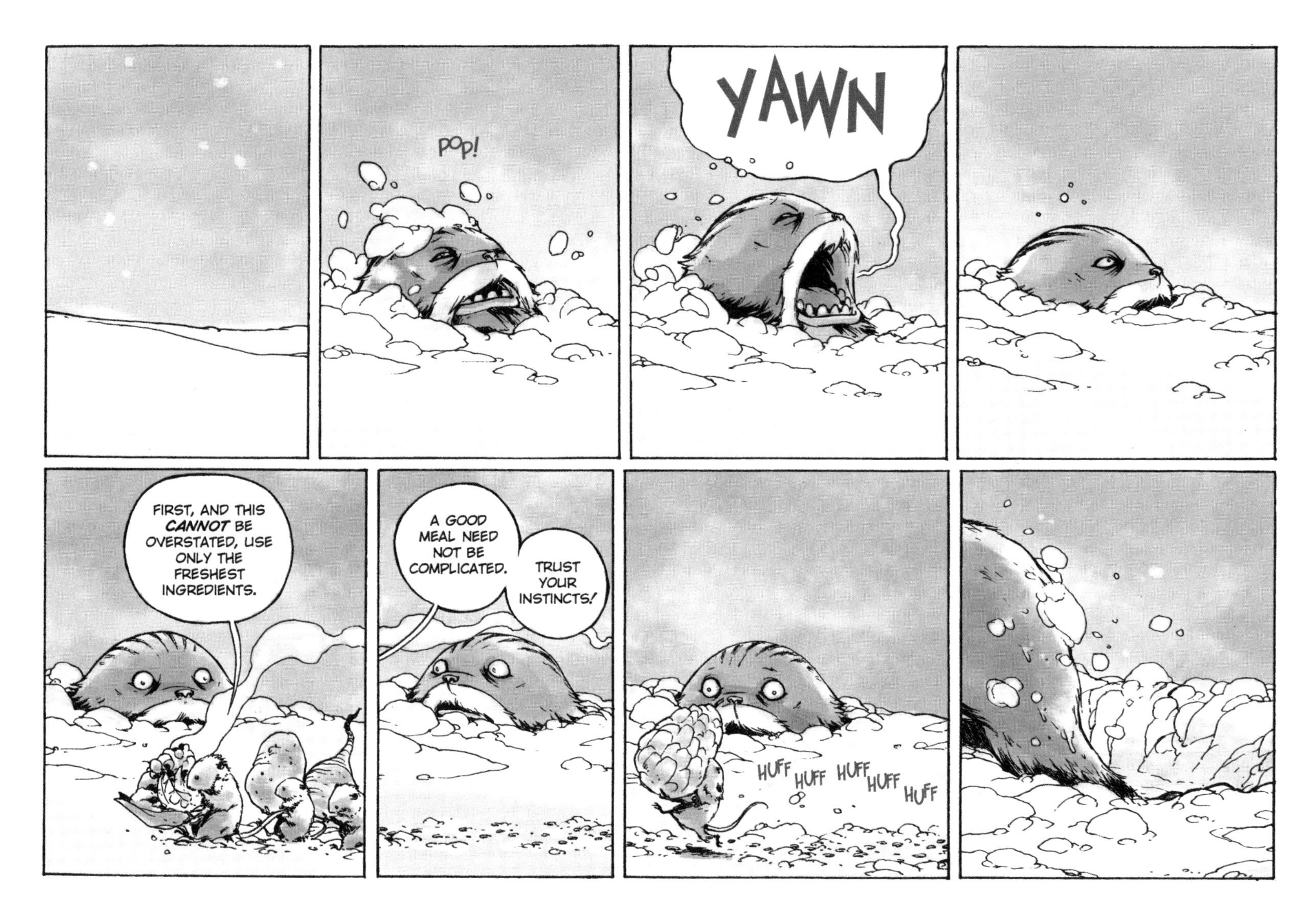
POP!
YAWN
FIRST, AND THIS CANNOT BE OVERSTATED, USE ONLY THE FRESHEST INGREDIENTS.
A GOOD MEAL NEED NOT BE COMPLICATED.
TRUST YOUR INSTINCTS!
HUFF HUFF HUFF HUFF HUFF

SNIFF
SNIFF

RUSTLE

ANY FRUIT MAY BE USED IN A COMPOTE, BUT REMEMBER: THE FLAVOUR OF BLACK-CURRANTS DOES TEND TO DOMINATE!

GOOD, MATTHEW!
BUT WHAT DID YOU FORGET TO DO?
SNIFF SNIFF

I SMELL SOMETHING FUNNY.
NONSENSE! WHAT YOU SMELL IS THE NATURAL AROMA OF--

SPLOOSH

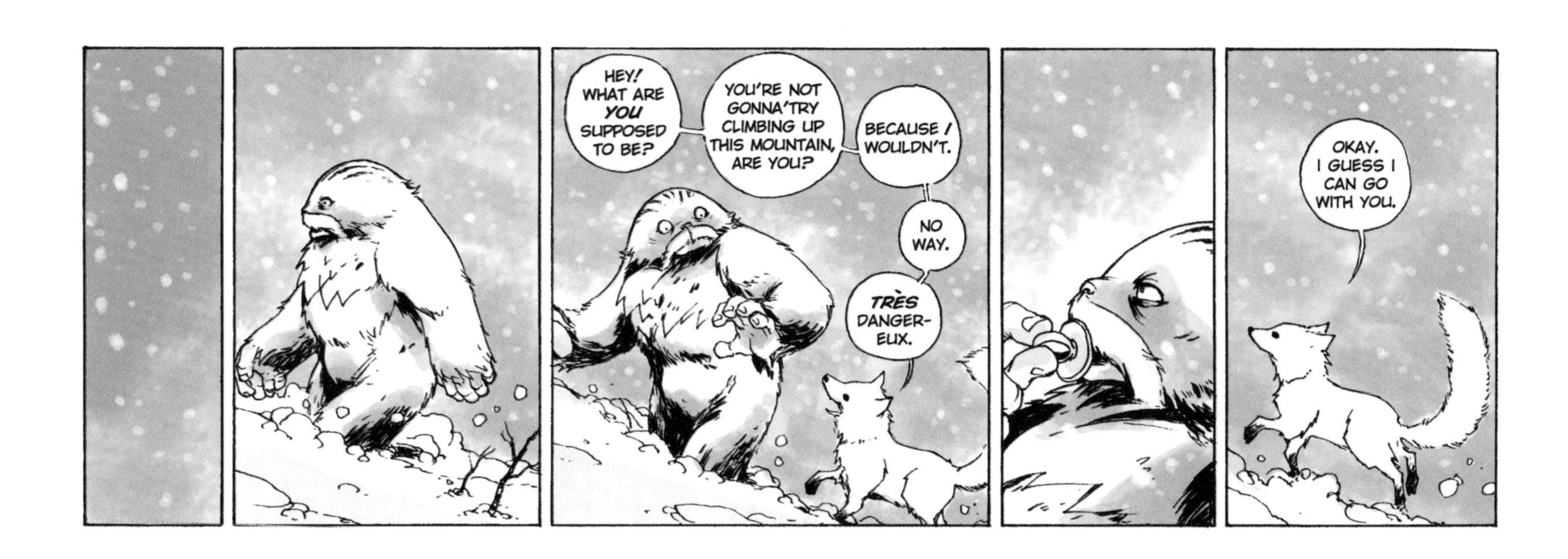
HEY! WHAT ARE YOU SUPPOSED TO BE?
YOU'RE NOT GONNA'TRY CLIMBING UP THIS MOUNTAIN, ARE YOU?
BECAUSE I WOULDN'T.
NO WAY.
TRÈS DANGER-EUX.
OKAY. I GUESS I CAN GO WITH YOU.

I BET YOU CAN'T GUESS HOW OLD I AM!
JUST *TRY* TO GUESS! I BET YOU CAN'T!
I'M ONE AND A HALF!

YOU *LOSE!*
I'VE GOT THREE OLDER BROTHERS, TOO!
YEAH, WE PRETTY MUCH HANG OUT TOGETHER ALL THE TIME.

I DON'T KNOW WHERE THEY ARE.

URGHH.
I'M OFF NOW, HONEY. I'LL BE HOME IN TIME FOR DINNER TONIGHT.

KISS?

DON'T FORGET TO PICK UP FRESH BERRIES ON YOUR WAY HOME TODAY.

EAT YOUR GRUBS, KIDS. I DON'T WANT YOU TO END UP LIKE YOUR FATHER.

FNOOF

YAWNNNNN

CRACK

HAPPY NEW YEAR!

MAN, AM I FULL!

YOU LOOK FULL, FRIEND! HEALTHY AND SATISFIED!
I AM!

WHERE DID YOU FIND SUCH A NUTRITIOUS AND WELL-MADE FEAST?
WHY, AT SISSI SKUNK'S OF COURSE!

SHE SERVES A VARIETY OF BERRIES, INSECTS, FRUIT, CHICKEN AND SMALL MAMMALS! EVERYTHING THE DISCERNING OMNIVORE COULD ASK FOR!

WOW! WHERE CAN I FIND HER?
SHE'S CON-VENIENTLY LOCATED AT SOUTH-BEND-IN THE-RIVER!

I FEEL KIND OF HUNGRY NOW.

I DON'T KNOW WHAT'S WRONG WITH ME.

I HAVE A GREAT FAMILY. I LOVE MY WIFE. MY KIDS. I DON'T KNOW. I FEEL...
I DON'T KNOW.

ARE YOU GOING TO SAY ANYTHING, OR WHAT?!

TELL ME ABOUT YOUR MOTHER.

HOOOOO

HA HA
IT'S JUST THE WIND!

YOU WERE SO SCARED, AND YOU'RE, LIKE, THREE TIMES BIGGER THAN ME!
YOU'RE LUCKY I'M HERE.

I ASKED MY BROTHERS ONCE WHERE THE WIND CAME FROM, AND THEY SAID IT CAME FROM THIS MOUNTAIN!

HEY! THAT'S PROBABLY HIM NOW!
ARE YOU THE WIND?

YUP.

HOOO

YOU'RE A LIAR.

I DON'T KNOW ABOUT THIS.

TODAY IS YOUR DAY, BERTRAND! I CAN FEEL IT!
REMEMBER WHAT DAD SAYS. THERE'S NO SHAME IN FAILURE IF NO ONE'S AROUND TO SEE IT!

I HAVEN'T STRETCHED YET! I NEED TO STRETCH!

I'LL START COUNTING DOWN FROM TEN.
NINE...
FOUR...
WAIT! WAIT!! OH GOD, YOU DON'T EVEN KNOW HOW TO COUNT!!

IS THIS THE TOP YET?

IT *IS!*
I WAS RIGHT AGAIN!

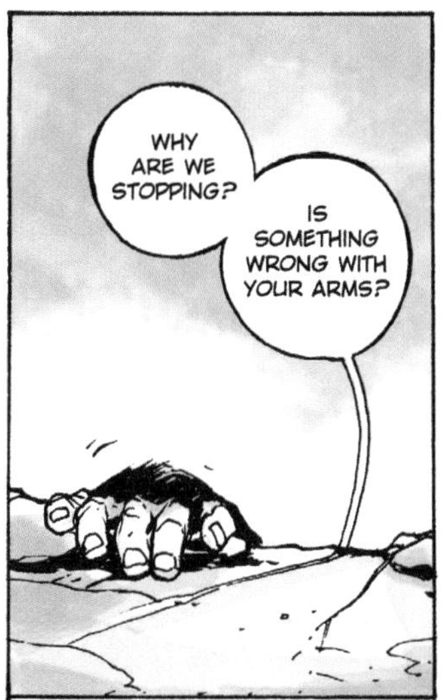
WHY ARE WE STOPPING?
IS SOMETHING WRONG WITH YOUR ARMS?

MAGNIFIQUE!
I DON'T THINK I'VE EVER BEEN ABLE TO SEE THIS MUCH OF ***ANYTHING*** BEFORE!
PANT
PANT
JUST WAIT 'TIL I--

UM...

A-ARE YOU THE WIND?

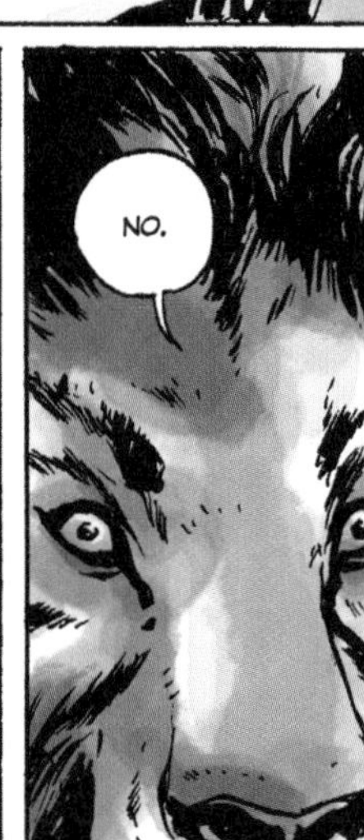
NO.

the STORY of
VIVOL & MOON BEAR
part two

AI! VIVOL!
WAKE UP! TIME FOR SHOW!

BEHAVE TODAY, EH?

SEE HOW FIERCE IS THIS BEAR!

HE KILLS THREE MEN BEFORE WE ARE ABLE TO CAPTURE HIM!

SEE HOW HE HATES!

BUT HE IS HUMBLED NOW!
HE KNOWS HE HAS A NEW MASTER!
HE DOES AS HE IS TOLD!
CRACK!

BACK IN YOUR CAGE, PIG!

WHAT MANNER OF CREATURE ARE YOU THAT YOU SCALE THIS MOUNTAIN AND THEN HIDE YOUR FACE?

OH, DON'T WORRY! HE DOES THIS ALL THE TIME!

LOOK AT ME.

PLOOMP

MY HEAD IS KILLING ME...

IT WAS A PARTY! WHAT DID SHE *EXPECT?* LIKE IT'S THE END OF THE WORLD BECAUSE I CAME HOME A BIT LATE AFTER A *PARTY!*
I DON'T EVEN DRINK THAT MUCH.

I DON'T.

I'M A *GOOD FATHER!*
PLEASE TRY TO RELAX.

THREE...
TWO...

HELLOO CHILDREN! SPREADING OUR WINGS THIS MORNING, ARE WE?
YES.
NO.
...NO.

MY GREGORY TOOK HIS FIRST FLIGHT WITH HIS FATHER JUST THE OTHER DAY! HE WAS A NATURAL! SUCH A LITTLE ATHLETE.

TRUDEL? IS THAT YOU? COME ON IN.
IT'S ME, DEAR! JUST ARRIVED!

I HEARD GREGORY CRASHED INTO TWO TREES AND THEN WET HIMSELF.
SOME ATHLETE.

DO YOU EVER FEEL LIKE THERE JUST AREN'T ENOUGH HOURS IN THE DAY?
WHAT DO YOU MEAN?

LIKE THERE JUST ISN'T ENOUGH TIME EVERY DAY TO DO ALL OF THE THINGS YOU NEED TO DO.

NOT REALLY.
I'M ALWAYS DOING EXACTLY WHAT I WANT TO BE DOING ***RIGHT NOW.***

YOU'RE PICK-ING STUFF OUT FROM BETWEEN YOUR TOES.
YES.

WAKE UP.
WAKE UP.
WAKE UP.
WAKE UP.
WAKE UP.
GOOD.
NOW LET ME SHOW YOU WHY YOU'RE HERE.

I FELT THAT A CHANGE WAS COMING, BUT IN WHAT FORM I COULD NOT FORESEE.
AND YOU, MY FRIEND, ARE SOME-THING OF A SURPRISE.

I HAVE KEPT WATCH FROM THIS MOUNTAIN-TOP FOR A VERY, VERY LONG TIME.
AS SOLE GUARDIAN OF THE
HOW LONG?

EXCUSE ME?
HOW LONG IS A ***VERY, VERY*** LONG TIME?
ARE YOU OLDER THAN MY MOM?

...YES.
...AND AS ***SOLE GUARDIAN*** OF THE CEDAR-

WAIT, ARE YOU OLDER THAN MY ***GRANDMA?***

HOLD UP THERE, BIG GUY!
ARE YOU ON THE LIST?
LIST?

YOU AIN'T ON THE LIST, YOU AIN'T GETTIN' NO HONEY.
GONNA' HAVE TO WAIT BEHIND THE LINE LIKE EVERYBODY ELSE.

WHERE IS LINE?
HEY, I DON'T MAKE THE RULES, BUDDY!

WOAH! SORRY ABOUT THAT, VIVOL! IT'S ANDY'S FIRST DAY ON THE JOB.
COME ON UP.
YOU'RE ALRIGHT, BUD.

the STORY of
VIVOL & MOON BEAR
part three

SPLORP

WAIT.

WE SHARE HOME NOW, BUT WE DO NOT SHARE EVERYTHING.
VIVOL EATS FIRST, ALWAYS.

BUT I AM NOT HUNGRY NOW, I THINK.
YOU GO AHEAD.

YOU HAVE LOST YOUR MAMA, YES?
I KNOW HOW THIS IS.
MY OWN MAMA WAS TAKEN FROM ME WHEN I WAS VERY SMALL, AS YOU ARE.
IT IS GOOD THAT WE REMEMBER, BUT SADNESS MUST COME TO AN END.

...WE MUST LEAVE ENOUGH ROOM IN OUR HEARTS FOR REVENGE.

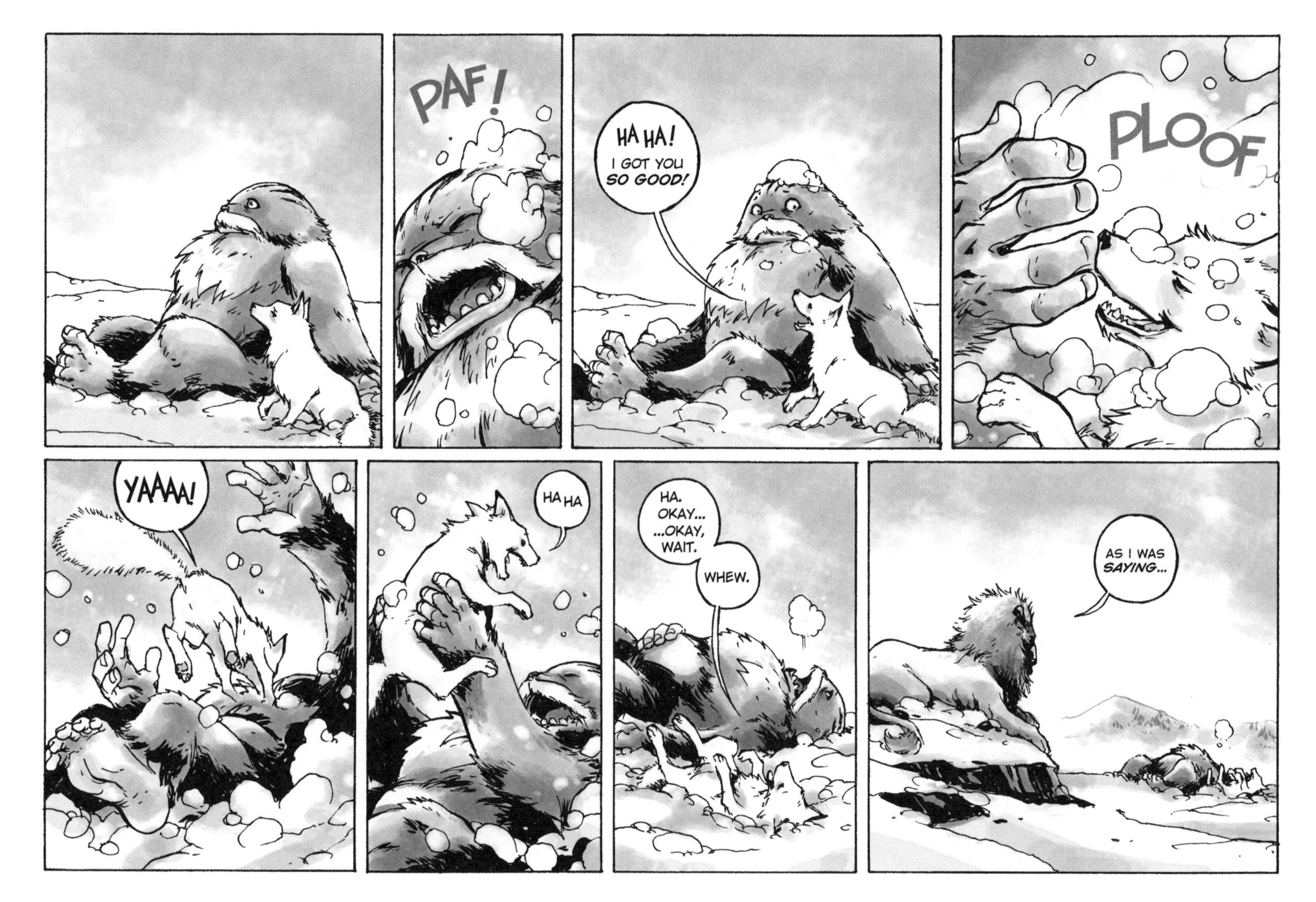
PAF!
HA HA!
I GOT YOU
SO GOOD!
PLOOF
YAAAA!
HA HA
HA.
OKAY...
...OKAY,
WAIT.
WHEW.
AS I WAS
SAYING...

I HAVE PROTECTED HER FOREST FOR UNTOLD YEARS...
...WATCHED OVER HER CHILDREN AND HER GREAT-GRANDCHIL-DREN.

BUT NATURE HAS SEEN FIT TO WELCOME A NEW SUITOR INTO HER ARMS.

AND YOU...

...YOU MUST CONVINCE HER THAT SHE'S MADE A MISTAKE.

IN SUCH MATTERS, THERE ARE CERTAIN... RULES BY WHICH I MUST ABIDE.
BUT YOU, MY FRIEND, ARE NEITHER FULLY MAN NOR BEAST.
I WILL SHOW YOU--

HEY, CAN WE GO HOME NOW? I MISSED SNACK TIME AND DINNER TIME. AND MY MOM SAYS--

SILENCE!

THE CITY OF MEN IS RULED BY A POWERFUL KING.
HIS BORDERS WILL EXPAND LIKE A DROP OF BLOOD IN THE GREAT RIVER.

I CAN KEEP HIM FROM REACHING US. BUT I NEED THREE THINGS, WHICH YOU MUST BRING HERE.

A LOCK OF THE KING'S HAIR...
...A TOKEN OF HIS FAITH...

...AND HIS NAME.

CHARLES.

TAKE CARE.

CHARLES? THAT'S YOUR NAME?
HOW DID THAT LION KNOW IT?
DID YOU TELL HIM?

YOU WERE PROBABLY GONNA' TELL ME NEXT, THOUGH, RIGHT?

MY MOM SAID I SHOULDN'T EVER TELL MY NAME TO STRANGERS.

IT'S ***TOWNSEN.***

ABOMINABLE.

TAKE NOTES, SON.
YOU CAN'T ACT LIKE A FOOL AND DO AS YOU PLEASE AND EXPECT TO SURVIVE IN THIS WORLD.

THAT BUFFOON DOWN THERE IS JUST PLAIN LUCKY.
THE REST OF US HAVE TO THINK AND PLAN IF WE WANT TO GET AHEAD.
AHEAD OF WHAT?

IT JUST BURNS MY TAIL THAT HE GETS AWAY WITH IT...

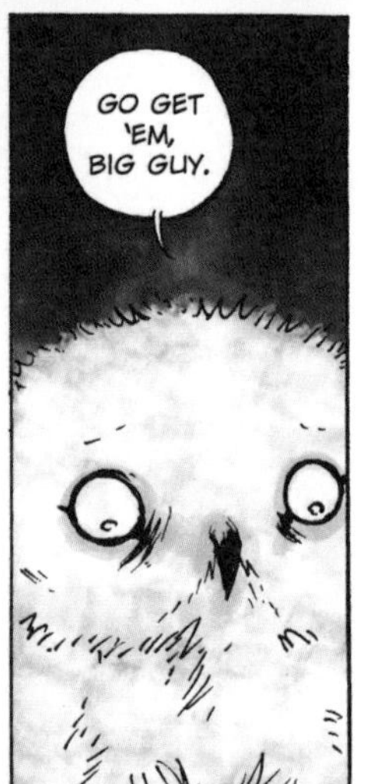
GO GET 'EM, BIG GUY.

IT'S NIGHT-TIME ALREADY? HOW DID THAT HAPPEN?
I DUNNO', GUY. HOW ABOUT WE DISCUSS IT DOWN AT THE WATERING HOLE?

WHAT?
ARE YOU CRAZY?! I CAN'T GO OUT DRINKING! I HAVE TO GET HOME TO DINNER!
MY WIFE IS GOING TO KILL ME!!

I WAS SUPPOSED TO PICK UP SOME THINGS FOR HER.
BUT I FORGOT WHAT THEY WERE!

OH, GOD! WHY CAN'T I REMEMBER?
MAYBE YOU'RE THIRSTY.

YOU'RE NOT GONNA' EAT THAT, ARE YOU?

YOU DON'T KNOW HOW LONG THAT THING'S BEEN DEAD. OR WHERE IT CAME FROM!
WHAT IF IT'S FULL OF POISON, OR-

GULP
GROSS!

LET'S FIND AN EVEN BIGGER ONE!

HOOOOOOOOOOOOOOOOOOOOOOOOOOOOOOOOOOOO
BROTHER...
SNRRK

YOU'RE IN MY SPOT.

HELLO?
WHERE DID YOU GUYS GO?
KOSEY? KINO?

HEY! THERE YOU ARE!
I'VE BEEN LOOKING ALL OVER FOR-

...YOU?

BACK AWAY. I'VE GOT DEADLY POISON IN MY GLANDS.

NOTHING PERSONAL, BUT I'VE GOT THREE MORE DAYS OF SQUATTING, ACCORD-ING TO FOREST LAW, BEFORE THIS BIT OF LAND IS LEGALLY MINE.
SOMETIMES THINGS CAN GET A LITTLE HOSTILE...

...THERE ARE CERTAIN PARTIES WHO WOULD JUST *LOVE* TO SWOOP IN HERE AND STAKE A CLAIM.

WHERE'S THAT KID YOU CAME HERE WITH?

BANG

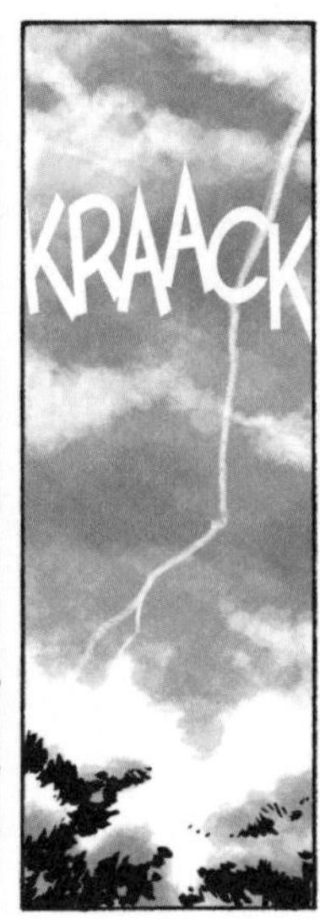
KRAACK

SOMETHING'S HAPPENED...

COME BACK INSIDE, CLARA.

SOMETHING'S HAPPENED TO MY SON.

CAN I COME INSIDE NOW? PLEASE?
HONEY?

UGH. IT'S RAINING AGAIN.

I HAD A MILLION THINGS TO DO TODAY, AND NOW IT'S ALL RUINED BECAUSE OF THIS STUPID WEATHER.
HOW MANY IS A MILLION?

A LOT. IT'S HIGHER THAN YOU COULD EVER COUNT.

BUT FORGET IT NOW. THANKS TO THIS RAIN, MY WHOLE WEEK IS SHOT.
MAYBE MY WHOLE MONTH.

WOW.
I HOPE THE RAIN DIDN'T RUIN MY BIRTHDAY NEXT YEAR.

CRACK
A BOOM

PLIP

WIND.

I AM AN OLD BEAR NOW, AND YOU DO NOT FOOL ME.

I SEE YOU FOR WHAT YOU TRULY ARE.

the STORY of
VIVOL
&
MOON
BEAR
part four

THE BIRDS FLY TO ANOTHER HOME FOR THE COLD MONTHS.

WE CANNOT FLY FROM HERE, BUT AT LEAST WE MAY REST A LITTLE, YES?
CIRCUS SLEEPS FOR THE WINTER, ALSO.

YOU ARE SO QUIET, LITTLE MOON BEAR.

ONE DAY YOU WILL TELL ME YOUR STORIES.

OKAY, YOU CAN COME BACK INSIDE NOW.
I NEED YOU TO LOOK AFTER THE KIDS WHILE I GO OUT TO-

...HOW LONG HAVE YOU TWO BEEN OUT HERE?
WHERE'S YOUR FATHER?

HE WENT TO GET BREAKFAST FOR US.
AND HE SAID TO TELL YOU THAT HE LOVES YOU AND... AND... THAT YOU'RE THE ONLY REASON HE GOES AWAY EVERY MORNING.

THE ONLY REASON HE ***GETS UP*** EVERY MORNING!
JEEZ, BERTRAND!
SORRY!

I HAVE A PROBLEM WITH PUBLIC SPEAKING.

ANY LUCK?
NO!

EVERY GIRL I ASK ALREADY SEEMS TO HAVE A DATE TO THE DANCE!

WHAT GIVES? DO I SMELL OR SOME-THING?!?

FOR GOD'S SAKE, MARIA. WHY DO WE EVEN BOTHER?

I KNOW THINGS HAVE BEEN REALLY MESSED-UP LATELY, BUT WE CAN MAKE THIS WORK. I KNOW WE CAN!

NO, MARIA!
DON'T YOU GO BACK TO HIM!!

YOU KNOW WHAT?
I DON'T EVEN CARE ANY MORE.
ABOUT ANY OF IT.

BUT... BUT ANDERS...

...I'M CARRYING YOUR CHILD!!

WHAT?!?
WHEN DID THIS HAPPEN??!
SHHH!

HE'S CHEATING ON YOU!!!
SOB
WOULD YOU RELAX?
I KNEW YOU WERE TOO SENSITIVE FOR THE THEATRE!

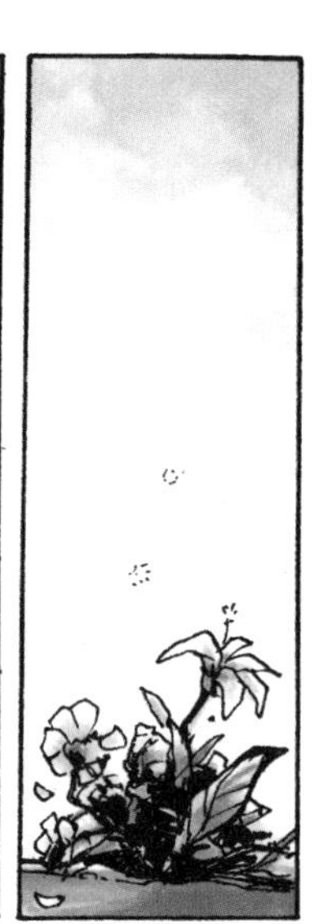

WHO NEEDS A DATE FOR THE DANCE, ANYWAY?
LICK

IT'D BE CRAZY TO TIE SOME-THING THIS GOOD DOWN TO JUST ONE WOMAN!
SLICK

HMM?
OH, THIS?
JUST A LITTLE TWO-STEP I PICKED UP IN MY YEARS ABROAD.

I CAN SHOW YOU MORE, MY SWEET.
SO MUCH MORE.
BUT NOT HERE.

OH, MY! AREN'T YOU TALENTED!
MOTHER! A LITTLE PRIVACY, PLEASE?!

YOU'RE GETTING SO BIG.
SOON WE WON'T EVEN RECOGNIZE YOU ANY MORE.

EVERY NIGHT I THINK ABOUT YOU AND WONDER HOW YOU'RE DOING.
IF YOU'RE EATING PROPERLY.

OH, WE SHOULD NEVER HAVE LEFT HIM ALONE.
HE'S SO FRAGILE.
HE'S FINE.
AND HE'S NOT GOING TO EMBARRASS US.

WILL YOU, SON?

WILL YOU?

IT'S THE YEAR OF THE RAT!
AND IT'S ABOUT TO END!

HEY! LISTEN UP, EVERY-BODY! ARE WE GONNA' LET THIS YEAR COME TO A CLOSE WITHOUT SOME PROPER RAT-RECOGNITION?
IF ANYTHING, RATS WERE UNDER-APPRECIATED THIS YEAR!

WHAT ABOUT YOU, FRIEND? YEAR OF THE RAT??
DON'T TOUCH ME!!

AWW, YEAH! THE RATS ARE BRINGIN' IT BACK FOR ANOTHER-

SWOOP

HEY, MAN!
YOUR FEATHERS! YOUR FEATHERS ARE GETTING AWAY!

IF YOU HURRY YOU CAN STILL CATCH THEM!

...AND IF YOU COLLECT THEM IN ORDER, THEY'LL BE WORTH EVEN MORE!

YOU'RE TERRIBLE.
I KNOW.

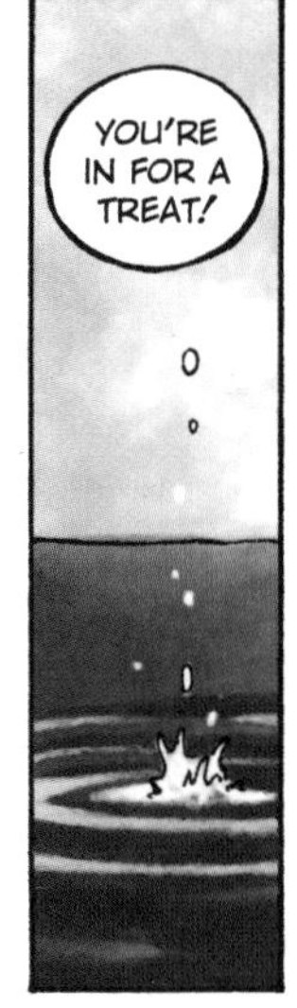
YOU'RE IN FOR A TREAT!

THIS IS SOME OF THE FINEST DRINKING WATER IN THE WHOLE CEDAR FOREST.

GLACIAL SPRINGS ENTER THE CANYON TRIBUTARY HERE BEFORE FLOWING INTO THE GREAT RIVER, PASSING OVER PEAT BOGS AND A VARIETY OF MINERALS.

IN FACT, IT'S NOT UNCOMMON TO TASTE SUBTLE HINTS OF **APPLE** IN THE...
PLOONK
IN THE, AH...

UM..

TIME IS WASTING, CHARLES.

NOTHING CAN BE DONE TO SAVE YOUR FRIEND.
AND YOUR PATH IS TOO IMPORTANT TO AFFORD WEAK-NESS.
EVEN IN MOURNING, YOU MUST KEEP ONE EYE ON THE FUTURE.

MOVE ON.
BEFORE IT'S TOO LATE.

HELLO?
ARE YOU QUITE WELL?

SO?
WHO ARE YOU FOR, THEN?

I'M A **ROMPERS** FAN, OF COURSE.
MUST SUPPORT THE LOCAL BOYS!
BUT THE **SOUTH-BEND SLIDERS** HAVE A GOOD TEAM THIS YEAR.
MUNCH MUNCH

CRISP?
DON'T EAT ME!

ARE WE LATE?
WHAT'S THE SCORE?
WHO'S THIS GUY?
SOUTH-BEND'S MASCOT, I THINK. HE'S KEEPING SUSPICIOUSLY MUM.

TWENTY SECONDS LEFT ON THE CLOCK, AND IT LOOKS LIKE THE ROMPERS AREN'T GOING TO BE ABLE TO CLOSE THE GAP.

WAIT...
SHIPLEY'S SURFACED FROM THE NARROWS, AND... HE'S GOT THE BALL!

OVER TO WENHAM NOW...
WENHAM BREAKS LEFT AROUND COOKE..
HE'S GOT A CHANCE IF HE CAN JUST...

SCORE!

EPIC MATCH, BOYS. ABSOLUTLEY CRACKING!
FIRST ROUND'S ON ME!

LET'S SEE HOW A SOUTH-BENDER HOLDS HIS-
WHERE'D HE GET OFF TO?

OKAY! I DROPPED THE KIDS OFF AT SCHOOL!

ARE YOU STILL MAD AT ME?

I'M NOT MAD AT YOU.
I JUST FEEL LIKE I NEVER SEE YOU ANY MORE.
WE WAKE UP, YOU GO TO WORK, AND YOU COME HOME IN THE MIDDLE OF THE NIGHT.

ANYWAY, YOU'RE HERE TODAY.

HAPPY ANNIVERSARY, HONEY.
KISS

IT'S ALL QUITE SIMPLE.

WE PERCEIVE TIME TO BE A FORWARD-MOVING STREAM, LIKE THIS RIVER.
BUT THIS IS MERE MOVEMENT. MOTION THROUGH SPACE.

INDEED, OUR MINDS FRAME THESE MO-TIONS INTO VIRTUAL ***MOMENTS***, BY WHICH WE ANALYZE AND PLAN OUR LIVES.
WE NEED ONLY STOP ANTICIPATING OUR FUTURES AND REFLECTING UPON OUR PASTS TO BE TRULY CONTENT.

DO YOU FOLLOW?

THANKS FOR NOT EATING ME.

WHAT ARE YOU DOING?

I'M TRYING TO ***MEDITATE.*** IT'S VERY HARD.
MOSTLY BECAUSE I CAN'T STOP THINKING ABOUT ALL OF THE LITTLE CHORES AND THINGS I HAVE TO DO TODAY.

BUT IN A FEW YEARS, AND WITH A LOT OF PRACTICE, I'LL BE ABLE TO ***QUIET MY MIND*** ENOUGH TO...

VIVOL?
ARE YOU BUSY?
I NEED SOME ADVICE.

VIVOL IS HERE ALWAYS, LITTLE ONE.
WHAT IS QUESTION?

I THINK I MIGHT BE IN LOVE.
BUT I DON'T KNOW HOW TO TELL HER!
I TRIED GIVING HER FLOWERS, AND...

VIVOL CANNOT HELP YOU WITH THIS.

BUT...

the STORY of VIVOL & MOON BEAR
part five
CLAP CLAP CLAP CLAP CLAP

OUR YOUNGEST BEAR THINKS SHE IS AN ACROBAT!
HOW DOES SHE GET INTO SUCH MISCHIEF?

NO!
IT IS TOO HIGH!

BE SILENT, PIG!
YANK!

HUT, MOON BEAR!
UP!

CLAP CLAP CLAP CLAP CLAP CLAP CLAP CLAP CLAP CLAP CLAP

CLAP CLAP CLAP
THANK YOU.

CLAP CLAP CLAP CLAP
THANK YOU FOR KEEPING HER SAFE...

FAIR LADY, MAY I THUS MAKE FREE TO OFFER YOU MY ARM AND COMPANY?

I AM NO LADY, AM NOT FAIR, CAN WITHOUT ESCORT HOME REPAIR.

THIS IS *BORING.*
SHHH!
HERE COMES THE DEVIL!

THIS GIRL MUST WIN FOR ME! DOST HEAR?
WHICH?
SHE WHO BUT NOW PASSED.

O'ER SUCH AS SHE I'VE NO CONTROL!

BY STORM WE CANNOT TAKE THE FORT, TO STRATAGEM WE MUST RESORT.

"TO STRATAGEM WE MUST RESORT". HMMMMM.
I'M GOING HOME. HOW'S *THAT* FOR A 'STRATAGEM'?

LOOK, GUY. I'M ONLY HERE BECAUSE WORK SAID I HAD TO HAVE A MANDATORY PSYCH TEST.
I DON'T NEED *THERAPY*.

NO ONE SAID YOU DID.
NOW. LET'S GET TO KNOW EACH OTHER, SHALL WE?

YOU'RE *REALLY* SMALL.
WHAT'S TO STOP ME FROM EATING YOU?

IF I'M REMOVED FROM THIS SEAT BY FORCE, TWO THOUSAND ANGRY ROACHES WILL DROP FROM THE TREES ABOVE, COMPLETELY BLANKETING THIS AREA.
YOU'LL BE TORN APART WITHIN SECONDS.

WHAT?! FOR *REAL*?!
NOTE: SUBJECT IS EXTREMELY GULLIBLE...

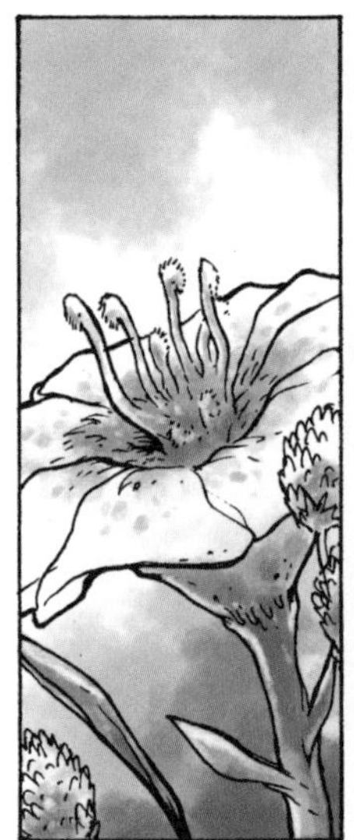

SHAKE
SHAKE
SHAKE

SHAKE
SHAKE
SHAKE

CHA!

MAYBE IF YOU JUST ***TOLD*** US WHERE YOU FOUND THE NECTAR...

COURAGE IS A COMPLEX QUALITY.
YOU SEEM TO EXEMPLIFY *PHYSICAL* COURAGE...
WHILE I WOULD MORE LIKELY BE *MORALLY* COURAGEOUS IN THE FACE OF...

!

SPLOOSH

HEH. *FIGHT-OR-FLIGHT* RESPONSE.
BIOCHEMICAL. AND PERFECTLY NORMAL IN ANY LIFE-THREATEN-ING SITUATION.

GOOD LUCK, MY FRIEND!
IF IT'S ANY CONSOLATION, I'LL BE EMBARRASSED ABOUT THIS ONCE THE ADRENALINE WEARS OFF!

AWK

AWK
AWK

AWK
AWK
AWK
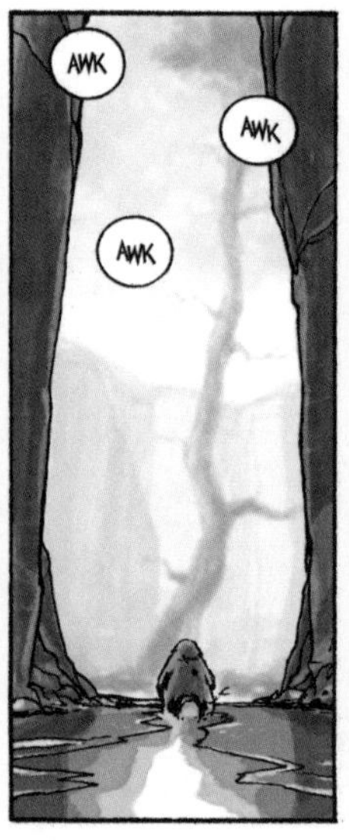
AWK
AWK
AWK

CRACK

AWK
HOOOOO
AWK
AWK

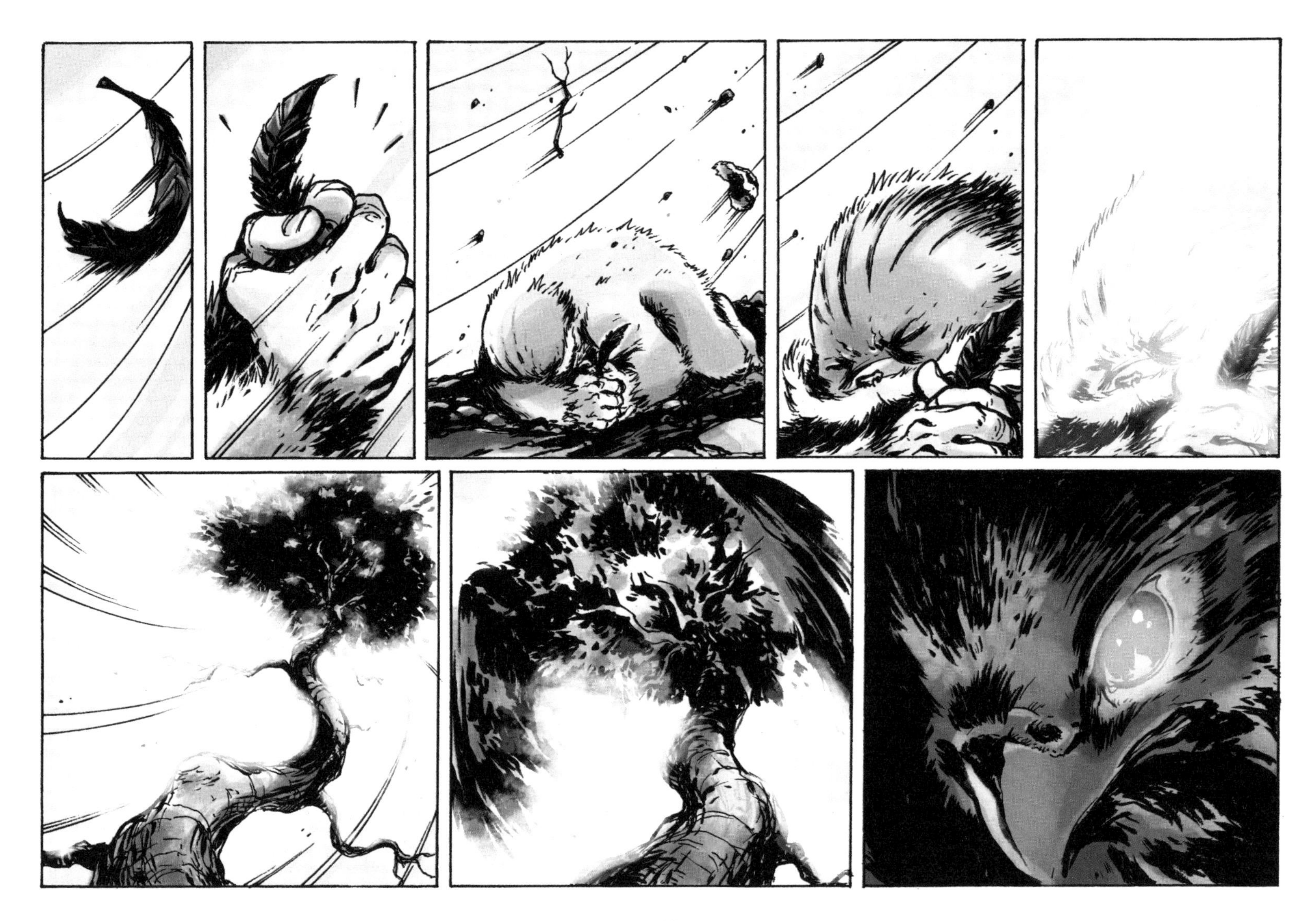

YOU HAVE SOMETHING THAT BELONGS TO ME.

ALRIGHT, CHILDREN!
TODAY YOU'RE GOING TO TAKE YOUR FIRST SHORT FLIGHT ALL THE WAY DOWN TO THE NEXT BRANCH.
I KNOW IT CAN BE SCARY, BUT WE'VE BEEN OVER THE THEORY, SO YOU SHOULDN'T HAVE ANY PROBLEMS.
QUESTIONS?
NO, MRS. SANDERSON.

I'LL SEE YOU TWO LOSERS AT THE BOTTOM!
SHUT UP, GREGORY.

HOOOOO

ABORT FLIGHT!
WHERE ON EARTH DID THIS WIND COME FROM?

HEH. TOO BAD!
I WAS LOOKING FORWARD TO COASTING ON SOME OF THOSE SWEET THERMALS!
HEH.
I'M TOO RELIEVED TO HATE HIM RIGHT NOW...

THE FEATHER, CHARLES.
GIVE IT TO ME.

THE VOICES ON THE WIND TELL ME EVERYTHING.
I KNOW YOUR NAME AS I KNOW YOUR THOUGHTS.
I FEEL YOUR TREMBLING IN MY VERY ROOTS.

GIVE ME WHAT IS MINE AND RETURN TO YOUR SIMPLE WAYS.

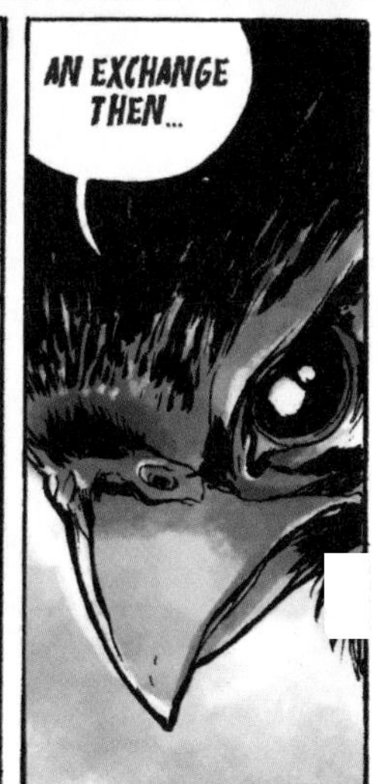
AN EXCHANGE THEN...

RETURN THE FEATHER...
...AND I WILL MAKE REAL YOUR HEART'S DEEPEST DESIRE.

WHAT IS IT YOU SEEK?
TELL ME.

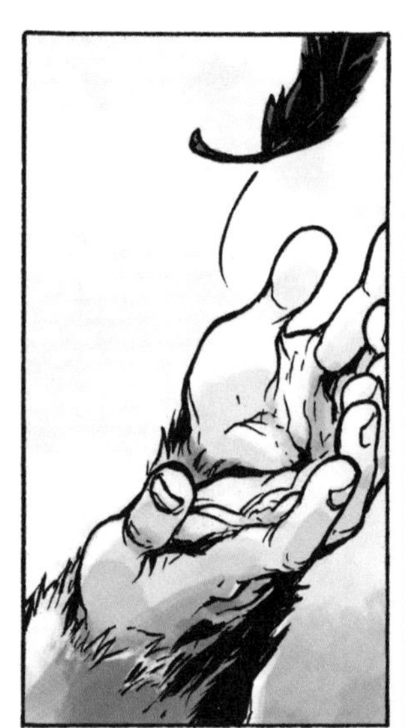

THE TERMS ARE ACCEPTED.

BEST OF LUCK, CHARLES.
SHOULD YOU DECIDE TO CONTINUE ON MY BROTHER'S ERRAND, KNOW THIS...

...THE TRUTH IS OFTEN BURIED DEEPER THAN WE REALIZE.

SNIFF
SNIFF
SNIFF
SNIFF
DO YOU... HAVE YOU SEEN OUR BROTHER?
WHERE IS HE?
WHERE'S *TOWNSEN?*

DO YOU EVER MISS MOM?

YOUR MOTHER WAS A FINE WOMAN, SON.
A *FINE* WOMAN.

BUT EVEN THOUGH SHE'S NOT COMING BACK, WE'RE STILL A *FAMILY*.
NEVER FORGET THAT.

I WON'T.

TITLES

THE ABOMINABLE CHARLES CHRISTOPHER
continues every week, online at
www.abominable.cc

A BRAND NEW EPISODE EVERY WEDNESDAY!

WHAT?! *WHERE?*

IS THIS SOME KIND OF TRICK?